THE (X) FILES™

CREATED BY CHRIS CARTER

Night Lights

Writers
John Rozum

Kevin J. Anderson

Artists
Charles Adlard

Gordon Purcell

D1088134

TITAN BOOKS

CREATED BY CHRIS CARTER

THE X-FILES:
NIGHT LIGHTS
ISBN 1 85286 808 2

Cover and chapter heading illustrations by Miran Kim
Edited by Jim Salicrup and Dwight Jon Zimmerman

Published by Titan Books Ltd
42 - 44 Dolben St
London SE1 OUP

British Library Cataloguing-In-Publication data. A catalogue record for this
book is available from the British Library.

First edition: March 1997
10 9 8 7 6 5 4 3 2 1

Printed and bound in Great Britain by Stephens and George Ltd, Merthyr
Industrial Estate, Dowlais, Merthyr Tydfil.

THE (X) FILES™

NIGHT LIGHTS

John Rozum • Writer
Charles Adlard • Artist
John Workman • Letterer
Digital Chameleon • Colour Design & Rendering

FAMILY PORTRAIT

Kevin J. Anderson • Writer
Gordon Purcell • Penciller
Josef Rubenstein & Co. • Inkers
John Workman • Letterer
Digital Chameleon • Colour Design & Rendering

THIN AIR

John Rozum • Writer
Gordon Purcell • Penciller
Josef Rubenstein • Inker
John Workman • Letterer
Digital Chameleon • Colour Design & Rendering

NIGHT LIGHTS

PART ONE

pbeepbeepbeep beepbeepbeepbeeph

AUGUST 11, 1996
10:23 P.M.
BROWN MOUNTAIN, NC

DOCTOR MEAGHER? HI, I'M DANA SCULLY. WE SPOKE ON THE PHONE.

CHARLOTTE, PLEASE. THANK YOU FOR COMING.

THE *POLICE* TOLD ME I'D HAVE TO WAIT UNTIL THIS AFTERNOON TO FILE A *MISSING PERSON'S REPORT.* THEY SAID THAT, DESPITE ALL OF THE STAFF'S CARS STILL BEING PARKED OUTSIDE, THERE WAS NOTHING HERE TO INDICATE *FOUL PLAY.*

MY INTUITION WAS TELLING ME THAT SOMETHING WAS VERY *WRONG* HERE.

AUGUST 13, 1996
1:06 P.M.
BROWN MOUNTAIN, NC

ONE OF THE PEOPLE IN MY DEPARTMENT TOLD ME THAT SINCE THIS INSTALLATION BELONGS TO THE FEDERAL GOVERNMENT, I SHOULD GIVE THE *FBI* A CALL.

I *APOLOGIZE* IF I APPEAR...

...TO BE OVERREACTING, AND I HOPE THAT I AM, BUT SOMETHING TELLS ME THAT I'M *NOT.*

NO, NOT AT ALL. DON'T BE SILLY.

TELL ME WHAT YOU *THINK* MAY HAVE HAPPENED.

I DON'T KNOW. ALL I KNOW IS SOMEONE *SHOULD* BE HERE AT ALL TIMES. I TRIED CALLING ALL DAY YESTERDAY, BUT THERE WAS *NO ANSWER.* WHEN I TRIED EVERYONE AT HOME--THERE WAS NO ANSWER, EITHER.

FINALLY, *LAST NIGHT* I DROVE DOWN HERE IN PERSON. WHEN I GOT HERE, ALL OF THEIR CARS WERE SITTING OUTSIDE AND THEY WERE *NOWHERE* TO BE FOUND.

ARE *THESE* THE MISSING SCIENTISTS?

YES.

WHAT CAN YOU TELL ME ABOUT THEM?

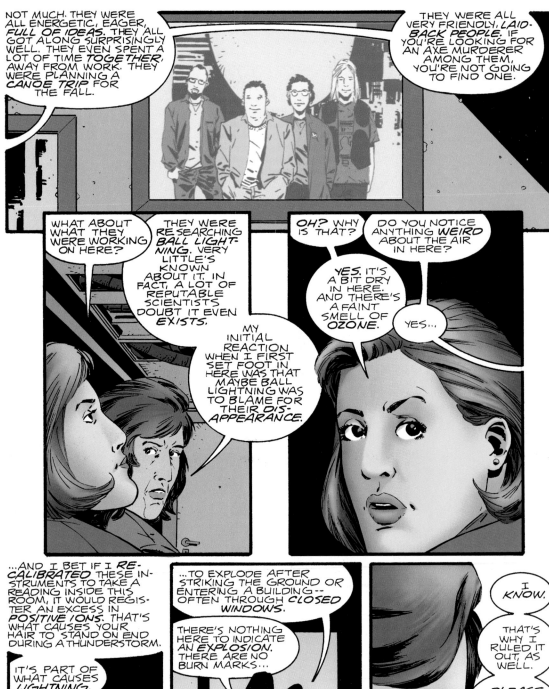

NOT MUCH. THEY WERE ALL ENERGETIC, EAGER, *FULL OF IDEAS*. THEY ALL GOT ALONG SURPRISINGLY WELL. THEY EVEN SPENT A LOT OF TIME *TOGETHER*, AWAY FROM WORK. THEY WERE PLANNING A *CANOE TRIP* FOR THE FALL.

THEY WERE ALL VERY FRIENDLY, *LAID-BACK PEOPLE*. IF YOU'RE LOOKING FOR AN AXE MURDERER AMONG THEM, YOU'RE NOT GOING TO FIND ONE.

WHAT ABOUT WHAT THEY WERE WORKING ON HERE?

THEY WERE RESEARCHING *BALL LIGHTNING*. VERY LITTLE'S KNOWN ABOUT IT. IN FACT, A LOT OF REPUTABLE SCIENTISTS DOUBT IT EVEN *EXISTS*.

MY INITIAL REACTION WHEN I FIRST SET FOOT IN HERE WAS THAT MAYBE BALL LIGHTNING WAS TO BLAME FOR THEIR *DIS-APPEARANCE*.

OH? WHY IS THAT?

DO YOU NOTICE ANYTHING *WEIRD* ABOUT THE AIR IN HERE?

YES, IT'S A BIT DRY IN HERE. AND THERE'S A FAINT SMELL OF *OZONE*.

YES...

...AND I BET IF I *RE-CALIBRATED* THESE INSTRUMENTS TO TAKE A READING INSIDE THIS ROOM, IT WOULD REGISTER AN EXCESS IN *POSITIVE IONS*. THAT'S WHAT CAUSES YOUR HAIR TO STAND ON END DURING A THUNDERSTORM.

IT'S PART OF WHAT CAUSES *LIGHTNING*.

BALL LIGHTNING HAS BEEN REPORTED...

...TO EXPLODE AFTER STRIKING THE GROUND OR ENTERING A BUILDING -- OFTEN THROUGH *CLOSED WINDOWS*.

THERE'S NOTHING HERE TO INDICATE AN *EXPLOSION*. THERE ARE NO BURN MARKS...

...AND NONE OF THE EQUIPMENT IS PHYSICALLY DAMAGED.

EVEN IF SUCH AN EXPLOSION HAD OCCURRED, IT STILL WOULDN'T EXPLAIN *WHY* THE SCIENTISTS HAVE ALL VANISHED WITHOUT LEAVING ANY REMAINS.

I *KNOW*.

THAT'S WHY I RULED IT OUT, AS WELL.

PLEASE FIND OUT WHAT HAPPENED TO MY SCIENTISTS.

WHAT IMPECCABLE *TIMING*, MULDER.

DIDN'T ANYONE EVER TELL YOU THAT THE *EARLY BIRD* CATCHES THE WORM?

AND YOU WONDER WHY I'M *LATE?*

ACTUALLY, SCULLY, I WANT TO CHECK ON *SOMETHING* THAT HAPPENED ABOUT A HUNDRED MILES WEST OF HERE.

A WOMAN DRIVING ALONG THE HIGHWAY WAS CAUGHT IN WHAT SHE CALLED A BRIEF *SHOWER OF BLOOD.* WHEN SHE GOT OUT OF THE CAR, SHE SAW A REDDISH-ORANGE BALL OF LIGHT FLICKERING IN THE CLOUDS.

UNFORTUNATELY, ALL OF THE SO-CALLED *"BLOOD"* WASHED AWAY LONG BEFORE ANYONE COULD COLLECT A SAMPLE BUT *THIS* ALSO FELL OUT OF THE SKY AND STRUCK HER WINDSHIELD.

I DON'T BELIEVE IT... MULDER, COME HERE AND TAKE A *LOOK.*

THIS IS A PICTURE OF THE *MISSING SCIENTISTS.*

TAKE A LOOK AT THE *PIN* ON THE WOMAN'S JACKET.

IT LOOKS LIKE THE *SAME PIN.*

MULDER, THAT *CAN'T* BE THE SAME PIN.

IT'S *NOT* POSSIBLE.

IMPROBABLE, YES, BUT NOT IMPOSSIBLE. WE CAN CHECK IT FOR *FINGER-PRINTS*, TO BE SURE, BUT I HAVE A FEELING THAT THE ONLY ONES WE'LL FIND BELONG TO THE WOMAN WHOSE CAR THIS FELL ON.

HOW CAN THAT BE THE SAME PIN? HOW COULD IT TRAVEL OVER A HUNDRED MILES AND *FALL* OUT OF THE SKY?

FOR *CENTURIES*, THERE HAVE BEEN REPORTS OF *ANOMALOUS RAINS:* THINGS FALLING OUT OF THE SKY THAT SHOULDN'T.

FISH, SNAILS, MUSSELS, ROCKS... YOU AND I EXPERIENCED A *RAIN OF TOADS*.

THERE ARE *NO* EXPLANATIONS FOR THESE EVENTS, BUT WATERSPOUTS AND OTHER VIOLENT WINDS HAVE BEEN *SUSPECTED*.

THE WEATHER HERE TWO NIGHTS AGO WAS *CLEAR* WITH WIND SPEEDS OF LESS THAN FIFTEEN MILES PER HOUR.

OKAY, THEN *YOU* EXPLAIN IT.

IT'S BEEN A *HOT SUMMER.* IT COULD BE THAT THE *STRESS* OF THEIR WORK, COMBINED WITH HEAT EXHAUSTION, PRODUCED ABNORMAL OR ABERRANT BEHAVIOR.

DOCTOR MEAGHER SAID THAT IT'S NOT UNUSUAL FOR A *WEEK* TO GO BY WITHOUT CONTACT WITH THE RESEARCH STATION. IT COULD BE THAT THIS TIME THE STAFF *SECRETLY LEFT*, BUT *SOMEBODY* DECIDED TO CHECK UP ON THEM.

IT WOULD EXPLAIN HOW HER PIN WOUND UP OVER A *HUNDRED MILES* FROM HERE.

IT FELL OUT OF THE *SKY*.

BESIDES, IF THEY *DID* GO ON A ROAD TRIP, WHY ARE *ALL* THEIR CARS SITTING UP IN THE LOT OUTSIDE THE WEATHER STATION.

I DON'T KNOW--

MAYBE IT *WAS* BALL LIGHTNING.

LIGHTNING'S BEEN KNOWN TO REACH TEMPERATURES OF OVER *30,000 DEGREES FAHRENHEIT*-- MANY TIMES THE TEMPERATURE ON THE SUN'S SURFACE. THAT'S MORE THAN ENOUGH TO *INCINERATE* A HUMAN BODY.

BUT AS YOU POINTED OUT EARLIER, *NONE* OF THE EQUIPMENT SHOWED SIGNS OF EXPERIENCING THOSE TEMPERATURES.

I COULDN'T HELP *OVERHEARING* YOU, IF YOU'RE UFO BUFFS...

...AND ARE WONDERING ABOUT THOSE *RED LIGHTS* UP ON BROWN MOUNTAIN, THEY'RE *NOT* UFOs.

WHAT LIGHTS?

THE BROWN MOUNTAIN LIGHTS. PEOPLE HAVE SEEN THEM, GOING BACK INTO THE 1800s. THEY'RE A PRETTY COMMON SIGHT. THEY LOOK LIKE A RED BALL OF LIGHT, SO I CAN UNDERSTAND WHY ONE MIGHT THINK THEY'RE FLYING SAUCERS.

SO WHAT ARE THEY, THEN?

NOBODY KNOWS. BUT THEY'RE NOT FLYING SAUCERS. THERE'S NOTHING TO THEM, THEY'RE *JUST* LIGHT.

BALL LIGHTNING, MAYBE?

I DOUBT IT.

AS FAR AS I KNOW, BALL LIGHTNING DOESN'T TRAVEL FROM THE GROUND *UP*.

THERE HAVE BEEN STUDIES OF THE *BROWN MOUNTAIN LIGHTS,* AND IT IS BELIEVED THAT THEY ARE NOTHING MORE THAN THE *REFLECTION* OF CAR HEAD-LIGHTS ON THE HIGHWAY, OR THE LIGHTS OF *DISTANT TOWNS.*

TAIL LIGHTS *MIGHT* REFLECT RED, BUT WHY WOULD HEAD-LIGHTS?

REFRACTION?

AUGUST 12, 1996
3:41 P.M.
MORGANTON, NC

MAYBE. BUT THESE LIGHTS HAVE BEEN SEEN AS FAR BACK AS THE *MID-1800s.* THERE WEREN'T ANY CARS BACK THEN.

WHAT ABOUT "*EARTH LIGHTS*"?

I'M AFRAID I *DON'T...*

A *TECTONIC STRESS THEORY* HAS BEEN PROPOSED WHICH SUGGESTS THAT *STRAIN FIELDS* WITHIN THE EARTH'S CRUST, WHERE FAULT LINES OCCUR, PRODUCE *ELECTROMAGNETIC CHARGES* WHICH CREATE BODIES OF LIGHT.

IT SOUNDS A LITTLE *FAR-FETCHED,* BUT WHO KNOWS?

EVEN IF THAT *DID* EXPLAIN THE BROWN MOUNTAIN LIGHTS, LIGHTS ARE *NON-CORPOREAL* AND DO NOT ABDUCT SCIENTISTS.

...AND THAT'S *ALL* I CAN TELL YOU. I DON'T EVEN KNOW *HOW* I GOT HERE.

MORGANTON HOSP

AUGUST 13, 1996
3:15 P.M.

DOCTOR MEAGHER BROUGHT YOU IN. SHE'S THE ONE THAT *FOUND* YOU.

THANKS.

HOW LONG AM I GOING TO HAVE TO *STAY* HERE?

ACCORDING TO YOUR *CHART*, YOU HAVE A SLIGHT CONCUSSION, SOME MINOR ELECTRICAL BURNS, AND SOME TEMPORARY RETINA DAMAGE FROM STARING AT A *BRIGHT* LIGHT.

I THOUGHT IT WAS JUST BECAUSE I LOST MY *GLASSES*.

YOU'LL BE HERE FOR A COUPLE MORE DAYS, AT LEAST.

AGENT SCULLY, AGENT MULDER, CAN I *SEE* YOU TWO FOR A MOMENT?

SURE. THANK YOU, KURT. GET BETTER QUICKLY.

I'LL DO MY *BEST.*

YOU'LL HAVE TO BE *PATIENT* WITH ME. MY JOB WITH THE U.S. METEOROLOGICAL SOCIETY IS MORE *ADMINISTRATIVE* THAN HANDS-ON IN NATURE.

SOME OF THIS EQUIPMENT HADN'T EVEN BEEN DEVELOPED THE LAST TIME I WAS IN THE *FIELD.*

TAKE YOUR TIME.

AUGUST 13, 1996
6:03 P.M.

IF WHAT KURT TOLD US REALLY HAPPENED, THEN WHY ISN'T THERE ANY *PHYSICAL* EVIDENCE?

IN NUCLEAR BLASTS, OFTEN TIMES THE BUILDING AT *GROUND ZERO* IS LEFT STANDING WHILE EVERYTHING AROUND IT IS *VAPORIZED.* IT COULD BE THE REVERSE OF THAT.

THEN WHY DIDN'T IT MELT THE *WINDOW* WHEN IT PASSED THROUGH IT?

THE HEAT REQUIRED TO *INCINERATE* A BODY SO COMPLETELY WOULD HAVE BEEN GREAT ENOUGH TO *MELT* MUCH OF THIS EQUIPMENT AND TO *BURN* THE WOOD AND PAPER.

MAYBE IT'S AN INTENSE, *LOCALIZED* HEAT.

I DON'T KNOW.

I *GOT* IT! EVERYTHING'S UP AND *RUNNING.*

I'M *DOWN-LOADING* THE BALLOON TRANS-MISSION DATA NOW.

beepbeepbeepb

WHAT DO THOSE *FIGURES* MEAN?

THEY'RE AN ACCOUNT OF *EVERY-THING* RANGING FROM BAROMETRIC PRESSURE, TEMPERATURES, WIND SPEEDS AND DIRECTION, AIR SAMPLE COMPOSITIONS, AND SO FORTH.

WHAT'S IMPORTANT TO US IS THE *ION COUNT.* WE SHOULD BE SEEING DRAMATION *FLUCTUATIONS* IN THE DISTRIBU-TION OF POSITIVE AND NEGATIVE CHARGED IONS.

ACCORDING TO THIS, EVERYTHING'S *NORMAL.* ONLY ZEUS COULD GENERATE A LIGHT-NING BOLT IN THAT ATMOSPHERE.

WHAT ABOUT THE *EQUIPMENT* ITSELF?

beep beep beep beep beep

IS THERE ANY-THING THAT COULD ALTER THE ION DISTRIBU-TION OR GENERATE A STATIC BUILD-UP?

NO. *NOTHING.* I LOOKED IT ALL OVER BEFORE I TURNED IT ON. EVERY-THING'S *WELL-GROUNDED.* THERE'S PLENTY OF INSU-LATION, AND SURGE PRO-TECTORS ARE EVERYWHERE.

WELL, IT WAS WORTH A *TRY.*

FHZZZZZZTTT

CHARLOTTE, CAN YOU TELL WHAT'S *CAUSING* THAT?

beepbeepbeepbeep

BALL LIGHTNING DOESN'T NEED A *CONDUCTOR.* SOMETHING MUST HAVE DRIVEN *UP* THE POSITIVE ION COUNT IN HERE, BUT I HAVEN'T THE FOGGIEST IDEA *WHAT.*

I THINK WE'D BETTER *GET OUT* OF HERE.

I THINK YOU'RE *RIGHT.*

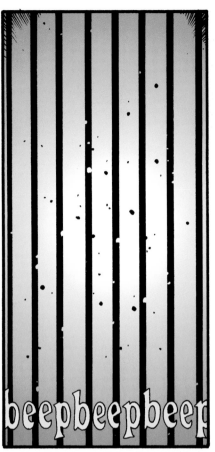

beepbeepbeepbeepbeepbeepbeep

eepbeepbeepbeep

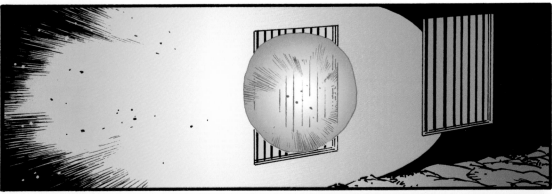

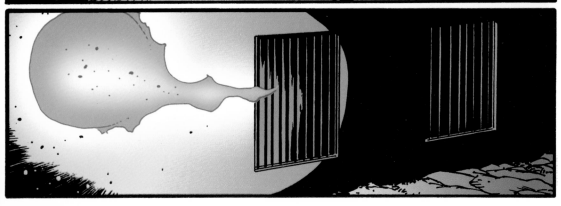

THE TRUTH IS OUT THERE™

OFFICE OF
THE LONE GUNMAN
AUGUST 13

"IN A 1913 ISSUE OF *THE STRAND* MAGA-
ZINE, A STORY WAS PUBLISHED BY *SIR
ARTHUR CONAN DOYLE* CALLED 'THE
HORROR OF THE HEIGHTS,' WHICH TOLD
THE TALE OF ATMOSPHERIC CREATURES
THAT ATTACKED AND KILLED PILOTS.

"THE STORY WAS *FICTION*, BUT WITH
CONAN DOYLE'S INTEREST IN THE PARA-
NORMAL, WHO'S TO SAY HE WASN'T BASING
IT ON A *GENUINE PHENOMENA?*

"*CHARLES FORT* NOTED REPORTS OF 'UN-
KNOWN LUMINOUS THINGS' SEEN IN THE
SKY, POSSIBLY 'LIVING THINGS THAT
OCCASIONALLY COME FROM SOME-
WHERE ELSE.'

"IN A 1959 *DENVER POST* INTERVIEW,
KENNETH ARNOLD... WHOSE SIGHTING
OF *NINE DISC-LIKE OBJECTS*
JUNE 24, 1947, MARKED THE BEGINNING
OF THE UFO AGE... REMARKED THAT
HE BELIEVED THAT UFOs WERE 'LIVING
ORGANISMS IN THE ATMOSPHERE' AND
HAD THE POWER TO
CHANGE THEIR
DENSITY...   "...AND
                   APPEARANCE.

"THE IDEA OF 'SPACE ANIMALS' EXISTING
IN THE UPPER ATMOSPHERE WAS EVEN
ENTERTAINED BY PROJECT SIGN, THE
U.S. AIR FORCE'S FIRST INVESTIGATIVE
UFO PROJECT.

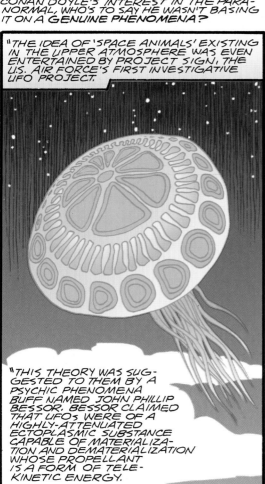

"THIS THEORY WAS SUG-
GESTED TO THEM BY A
PSYCHIC PHENOMENA
BUFF NAMED JOHN PHILLIP
BESSOR. BESSOR CLAIMED
THAT UFOs WERE OF A
HIGHLY-ATTENUATED
ECTOPLASMIC SUBSTANCE
CAPABLE OF MATERIALIZA-
TION AND DEMATERIALIZA-
TION WHOSE PROPELLANT
IS A FORM OF TELE-
KINETIC ENERGY.

"AS EVIDENCE, HE CITED REPORTED
FALLS FROM THE SKY OF FLESH AND
BLOOD.

"ON SEPTEMBER 26, 1950, TWO POLICE OFFICERS SAW WHAT THEY THOUGHT WAS A UFO LAND IN A FIELD OUTSIDE OF PHILADELPHIA. WHEN THEY INVESTIGATED, THEY DISCOVERED A SIX-FOOT LONG GELATINOUS MASS WHICH EVAPORATED WITHIN HALF AN HOUR.

"ON THE EVENING OF AUGUST 10, 1979, A FRISCO, TEXAS WOMAN WATCHED A BRIGHT LIGHT DESCEND NEAR A NEIGHBOR'S HOUSE. THE NEXT MORNING, THE NEIGHBOR FOUND THREE PURPLE BLOBS. ONE EVAPORATED IN THE SUNLIGHT."

THE OTHER TWO WERE SHIPPED OFF FOR ANALYSIS AND WERE DETERMINED TO BE INDUSTRIAL WASTE.

THERE'S BEEN A BIT OF SPECULATION ABOUT THE TRUTH OF THIS ANALYSIS, BUT FOR THE MOST PART, NOBODY'S REALLY DISCUSSED THE POSSIBILITY OF ATMOSPHERIC CREATURES EXISTING SINCE THEN.

THEN I GUESS I'LL BE BREAKING THE SILENCE.

THANKS, BYERS.

THINK ABOUT IT, SCULLY... AN ATMOSPHERIC LIFE FORM WOULD *EXPLAIN* WHY THERE WERE NO BODIES...

...AND HOW DOCTOR DENISE COOK'S *LAPEL PIN* CAME DOWN IN A SHOWER OF BLOOD OVER A HUNDRED MILES AWAY FROM WHERE SHE *DISAPPEARED.*

WE DON'T EVEN *KNOW* THAT THAT *WAS* BLOOD. IT WASHED AWAY BEFORE ANYONE THOUGHT TO COLLECT A *SAMPLE.*

YES, BUT WE *DO* KNOW THAT THE PIN BELONGED TO DOCTOR COOK. WE HAVE A DEFINITE MATCH OF HER *FINGERPRINTS* TO THOSE FOUND ON THE PIN.

WHAT IS IT, *EXACTLY,* THAT WE'RE SUPPOSED TO BE LOOKING FOR, MULDER?

PHYSICAL EVIDENCE. A SHOE OR WRISTWATCH BELONGING TO ONE OF THE OTHER SCIENTISTS. PURPLE GELATINOUS BLOBS.

SOMETHING THAT PROVES THAT THE BROWN MOUNTAIN LIGHTS ARE SOMETHING *MORE* THAN JUST LIGHTS.

SOMETHING TO SUPPORT THE *IDEA* THAT WE'RE DEALING WITH AN UNKNOWN LIFE FORM.

HOW CAN A CREATURE THAT'S *INTANGIBLE* ENOUGH TO PASS THROUGH A SOLID, CLOSED WINDOW *EAT* SOLID SCIENTISTS?

AND *WHY* WOULD IT ATTACK THE WEATHER STATION IN THE FIRST PLACE?

ANY *LUCK* FINDING ANY-THING?

NOT UNLESS YOU COUNT A LARGE PATCH OF *POISON IVY.*

=SIGH=

THE *PHONE* RANG WHEN I WAS HERE EARLIER. IT WAS DAVID BARGEN'S *FIANCÉE* CALLING FROM COLUMBIA UNIVERSITY.

SHE WAS *FRANTIC,* WONDERING WHY HE HADN'T CALLED HER FOR DAYS AND WHY HE WAS NEVER AT HIS APART-MENT.

I SAID HE WAS OUT IN THE *FIELD* WHERE HE COULDN'T BE REACHED.

IF I SAID HE WAS... *MISS-ING,* SHE'D WANT TO KNOW WHAT THAT MEANT. AND FRANKLY, I STILL DON'T KNOW THE ANSWER TO THAT.

I'M HOPING THAT ONE OF *YOU* WILL GIVE IT TO ME.

THE *SOONER,* THE BETTER.

I CAN APPRECIATE YOUR FRUSTRATION. WE DON'T HAVE AN *ANSWER* NOW.

BUT WE ARE WORKING ON IT.

WE MAY BE GETTING CLOSE TO THE *TRUTH.* TO GET ANY CLOSER, WE'RE GOING TO NEED *YOUR* HELP.

SURE. WHAT CAN I DO?

HAVE YOU BEEN ABLE TO *RECOVER* THE WEATHER BALLOON CARRYING THE *TRANS-MITTER* YET?

A *FARMER* PHONED IT IN FIRST THING THIS MORNING.

I HAVE SOMEONE PICKING IT UP AS WE SPEAK.

CHARLOTTE, CAN YOU TELL ME ANYTHING ABOUT ANY *OTHER EXPERIMENTS* THAT HAVE BEEN CONDUCTED AT THIS STATION?

HAVE THERE BEEN ANY *PREVIOUS* UNUSUAL OCCUR-RENCES?

NO. OVER THE YEARS, ALMOST *ALL* OF THE SCIENTISTS HERE HAVE SEEN THE BROWN MOUNTAIN LIGHTS. MOST OF THEM DISMISSED THE PHENOMENA AS ATMOSPHERIC TRICKS OF THE LIGHT, LIKE GLOWING SWAMP GAS.

GOOD. I'LL WANT TO TAKE A LOOK AT IT WHEN IT GETS HERE.

SURE. THERE ARE LOG BOOKS INSIDE COVERING THE LAST FIFTEEN YEARS.

IN FACT, IN THE EARLY EIGHTIES, *ONE* OF THE SCIENTISTS TRIED TO STUDY THEM FOR A *BRIEF TIME.*

WHAT DID HE *FIND?*

NOTHING.

HE DIDN'T FEEL THE RESEARCH WAS SUBSTAN-TIAL ENOUGH. HE ENDED UP GETTING BORED AND MOVED ON TO MAPPING AND STUDYING THE MICROCLIMATES IN THE AREA.

THE BALLOON'S HERE.

CHARLIE? WOULD YOU MIND IF WE *EXAMINED* THE BALLOON BY OUR-SELVES FOR A FEW MINUTES?

SURE. NO PROBLEM.

CORRECT ME IF I'M *WRONG*, BUT THESE THINGS USUALLY *DEFLATE* LIKE ANY OTHER HELIUM-FILLED BALLOON, DON'T THEY?

YES.

THE *STRESS MARKS* ALONG THE TEARS SUG-GEST THAT THIS ONE BURST FROM WITHIN.

MY GUESS IS THAT IT WAS CAUSED BY THE *RAPID HEATING OF THE GASSES WITHIN*, WHICH CAUSED THEM TO *EXPAND*.

IT STANDS TO REASON THAT IT WAS THE *SAME* HEAT SOURCE THAT FUSED THE TRANSMITTER.

ARE YOU GOING TO SUGGEST THAT THAT *RED LIGHT* WE SAW THE OTHER NIGHT DID *THIS?*

IF THAT LIGHT WAS ABLE TO INCINERATE A HUMAN BODY SO THAT THERE WERE NO PHYSICAL REMAINS, THEN *WHY NOT?*

BECAUSE *NONE* OF THE EQUIP-MENT INSIDE THE OUTPOST WAS FUSED, AND *ALL* OF IT WAS EXPOSED TO THE LIGHT.

I THINK THAT MAY BE BECAUSE NONE OF THE EQUIPMENT IN-SIDE WAS THE TARGET OF THE LIGHT. THE *SCIENTISTS* WERE.

AND YOU THINK THAT IT PURPOSEFULLY ATTACKED THIS *BALLOON?*

YES, AND I THINK I KNOW WHY.

TO BE CERTAIN, I'M GOING TO NEED TO TRY *SOMETHING*.

CHARLOTTE, CAN *YOU* RIG ANOTHER ONE OF THOSE *TRANS-MITTERS?*

NO, BUT I CAN HAVE ONE COURIERED TO US BY *TOMORROW MORNING*.

EXCUSE ME... AGENTS SCULLY AND MULDER?

AUGUST 14, 1996
5:20 P.M.
MORGANTON, PA

I'M POLICE CHIEF GEORGE HAMBRICK. I WAS WONDERING IF I COULD HAVE A WORD WITH YOU?

CHARLIE McCLINTOCK SAID HE *OVERHEARD YOU* TALKING ABOUT THE SCIENTISTS BEING ATTACKED AND ABOUT INCINERATED BODIES, SO I WENT UP TO ASK DR. MEAGHER WHAT WAS *GOING ON.*

IT'S JUST *ONE AVENUE* OF POSSIBILITY WE'RE EXPLORING.

THAT'S *SOME POSSIBILITY.* I ASKED DR. MEAGHER WHAT SORT OF CREATURE YOU THOUGHT IT MIGHT BE. YOU SHOULD HAVE SEEN MY *FACE* WHEN SHE TOLD ME IT WAS THE BROWN MOUNTAIN LIGHTS.

HAVE YOU EVER *SEEN* THE BROWN MOUNTAIN LIGHTS?

I *GREW UP* HERE. *OF COURSE* I HAVE. *DOZENS* OF TIMES.

THEY'RE A PRETTY *ODD SIGHT.* I'LL GIVE YOU THAT. SOMETIMES THEY MOVE AS IF THEY HAVE A MIND OF THEIR OWN. BUT YOU KNOW WHAT?

YOU DON'T *NEED* TO SUGGEST THEY'RE *ALIVE* TO MAKE THEM *STRANGE.*

THEY'RE *STRANGE ENOUGH* JUST BEING LIGHTS.

EXCUSE ME FOR CALLING INTO QUESTION YOUR *ABILITIES.* I KNOW THAT GETTING INTO THE FBI ISN'T *EASY.*

THE KIND OF DEDUCTIVE REASONING USED TO FIND THE *TRUTH*.

AS AGENT MULDER STATED, IT IS MERELY *ONE* AVENUE OF POSSIBILITY.

A NUMBER OF THINGS POINT TO THE *POSSIBILITY* THAT THE BROWN MOUNTAIN LIGHTS ARE A FORM OF ATMOSPHERIC ANIMAL. I CANNOT PROVE THIS RIGHT NOW, BUT I AM PLANNING A TEST FOR TOMORROW THAT SHOULD DETERMINE WHETHER OR NOT I AM *RIGHT*.

AND IF YOU ARE RIGHT? IF THE LIGHTS *ARE* LIVING ANIMALS?

THEN A TEAM OF *BIOLOGISTS* WILL BE ASSEMBLED TO STUDY THEM. IT WOULD BE A TREMENDOUS SCIENTIFIC BREAKTHROUGH.

BUT WHAT THE HELL KIND OF *DEDUCTIVE REASONING* DID YOU USE TO DETERMINE THAT THE BROWN MOUNTAIN LIGHTS ARE SOME SORT OF *LIVING CREATURE* AND THAT THEY ATE THE SCIENTISTS?

BUT AS WE'VE BOTH SAID, IT'S ONLY *ONE* POSSIBILITY WE'RE LOOKING AT.

AND, TO BE PERFECTLY HONEST, A *HIGHLY UNLIKELY* ONE.

ALL THE SAME, I'M SURE YOU *WON'T OBJECT* IF I ATTEND TOMORROW'S TEST?

THAT WAS PLEASANT. I CAN TELL THAT GUY'S GOING TO BE A *REAL* HELP.

I SHOULD *NEVER* HAVE MENTIONED THE TESTS TO HIM.

WHAT *ARE* THESE TESTS? WHAT DO YOU THINK YOU'RE GOING TO *PROVE*?

THE *OTHER NIGHT* WHEN THE LIGHT APPEARED WHILE WE WERE AT THE *OUTPOST*, IT DIDN'T ABANDON ITS APPROACH UNTIL I SHUT OFF THE *MONITOR* REPLAYING THE BALLOON TRANSMISSIONS.

I THINK IT'S POSSIBLE THAT THE *SOUNDS BROADCAST* BY THE TRANSMITTER COULD BE MISTAKEN FOR THE CREATURE'S *MATING CALL*.

DON'T LAUGH.

MULDER, IF ONE ACCEPTS THE LIGHTS AS LIFE FORMS, AS A POSSIBILITY, IT MIGHT MAKE SENSE...

IN 1988, A *GIANT SQUID* WAS DISCOVERED ATTACKING THE SUPPORT STRUCTURES OF A DEEP SEA OIL RIG. IT WAS THEORIZED THAT WHAT TRIGGERED THE ATTACK WAS THE *CLANGING SOUND* MADE BY THE RIG.

APPARENTLY, THESE CLANGING SOUNDS WERE VERY *SIMILAR* TO CERTAIN CALLS MADE BY SPERM WHALES; THE *NATURAL ENEMY* OF THE GIANT SQUID.

YOU CAN HARDLY CALL A BALL OF LIGHT AN *ENDANGERED SPECIES* IF YOU CAN'T BE CERTAIN IT'S ALIVE.

WE *CAN* STOP YOU. YOU'RE INTERFERING WITH AN FBI INVESTIGATION.

AND YOUR INVESTIGATION IS INTERFERING WITH THE SAFETY OF MY COMMUNITY.

PEOPLE *HIKE* IN THESE MOUNTAINS. THEY *CAMP* HERE. THOSE PEOPLE BRING A LOT OF *MONEY* INTO THE AREA; MORE THAN A HANDFUL OF GOVERNMENT- OR UNIVERSITY-PAID *SCIENTISTS*.

I'M *NOT* GOING TO JEOPARDIZE ANY MORE LIVES...OR THE *ECONOMY* OF THE AREA...IN ORDER TO PRESERVE WHAT MAY BE A *HOSTILE ENTITY*.

IF MULDER'S *RIGHT* AND THE TRANSMITTER IS WHAT'S BEEN TRIGGERING THE ATTACKS, THEN WE CAN EASILY PREVENT ANY *MORE* ATTACKS.

YEAH, BY WIRING EXPLOSIVES TO THE TRANSMITTER AND BLOWING THE LIGHT BACK TO *HELL*.

WE *CAN'T* LET YOU DO THAT.

HEY!

MULDER!

beepbeepbee beepbeepbeepbeepbeep

DAMN.

THE ACTIVATOR SWITCH IS *BROKEN.* IT CAN'T BE TURNED OFF.

DAMN IS *RIGHT.* GIVE ME THE TRANS-MITTER.

YOU'LL HAVE TO *DESTROY* IT.

beepbeepbeepbeepbeepbeepbeep

ALL IN *OUE* TIME.

SHERIFF, *LOOK!*

HAMBRICK, DON'T BE AN *IDIOT.* SMASH THE TRANS-MITTER BEFORE IT'S TOO LATE.

beepbeep

MAYBE YOU SHOULD *LISTEN* TO HIM, SHERIFF. IF THAT'S THE WORK OF GOD, THEN SURELY IT'S HIS *WRATH.*

beepbeep beepbeepbeepbeep

BASED ON WHAT I SAW DURING OUR TIME ON THE MOUNTAIN, I SUSPECT THAT I WAS RIGHT. WE WERE WITNESSING SOME UNKNOWN LIFE FORM. NONE OF THE OTHERS COULD AGREE ON WHAT THEY SAW, AND SO CERTAINTY IN CLASSIFYING THE BROWN MOUNTAIN LIGHTS HAS ELUDED US. THE TRUTH REMAINS A MYSTERY.

I KNOW THAT SCULLY STILL INSISTS IT WAS LITTLE MORE THAN AN ATMOSPHERIC TRICK OF THE LIGHT, BUT I SUSPECT HER BELIEFS AREN'T AS STRONG AS SHE LETS ON.

MEAGHER'S OFFICE CLOSED DOWN THE BROWN MOUNTAIN METEOROLOGICAL RESEARCH CENTER. NO BIOLOGISTS, NOR ANYONE ELSE WAS CALLED IN TO INVESTIGATE THE PHENOMENON.

IT LOOKS LIKE THE SETTING SUN.

OR ITS ATMOSPHERIC REFLECTION.

THE DISAPPEARANCE OF THE SCIENTISTS REMAINS UNEXPLAINED. DESPITE MY OWN CERTAINTY OF WHAT HAPPENED TO THEM, WITHOUT CONCLUSIVE EVIDENCE...

...IT IS DOUBTFUL THAT THE TRUTH BEHIND THEIR DISAPPEARANCE WILL EVER BE KNOWN.

THE END

TRUST NO ONE™

MISTER DUBAY? WE'RE FEDERAL AGENTS.

I UNDERSTAND YOU FOUND THE BODY OF MISTER HENRY FRANKLIN?

YES, I DID-- WHILE DELIVERING HIS MONTHLY ORDER OF PHOTO-CHEMICALS.

I TRIED TO KEEP AN EYE OUT FOR HIM, THOUGH... US OLD FARTS GOTTA STICK TOGETHER!

HENRY WAS QUITE AN ODD FELLOW... NO FRIENDS TO SPEAK OF...

I CAN GIVE YOU DIRECTIONS, BUT HIS PLACE ISN'T EASY TO FIND. HENRY LIKED IT THAT WAY.

DUBAY'S SERVICE STATION
DEADWOOD, SOUTH DAKOTA
10:53 A.M.

THIS IS A ROAD?

WE'VE DRIVEN PAST IT TWICE NOW. ACCORDING TO THE DIRECTIONS, THIS HAS GOT TO BE THE RIGHT TURNOFF.

I WONDER IF HANSEL AND GRETEL EVER MADE IT THIS FAR...

THIS CABIN IS SO ISOLATED, I CAN SEE HOW A SERIAL KILLER COULD HAVE WORKED FOR YEARS WITHOUT BEING CAUGHT...

MISTER FRANKLIN KEPT QUITE A *LIBRARY*.

I'LL BET HE HAD PLENTY OF TIME FOR *READING* OUT HERE...

BOOKS ABOUT *PHOTOGRAPHY* ...JOURNALS... AND SOME OF THESE I CAN'T READ AT ALL.

HE CERTAINLY WAS A GOOD PHOTOGRAPHER ...THESE IMAGES ARE *COMPELLING*...

ADMIRING *ART*, SCULLY?

JUST LOOK AT *THIS*, MULDER.

THEY'RE SO *REAL*, HYPNOTIC, AND LIFELIKE.

THESE PHOTOGRAPHS MUST HAVE BEEN TAKEN WITH THAT *OLD CAMERA*...

IT'S ALMOST AS IF YOU CAN FEEL FLASHES OF THEIR LIVES...

...HOW THEY *INTERTWINED*... WHAT THEY THOUGHT ABOUT EACH OTHER...

...AS IF THEIR *GHOSTS* ARE TRAPPED WITHIN THE FRAME.

I WONDER IF HIS SUBJECTS ARE ON YOUR *MISSING PERSON'S LIST*, MULDER...

MAYBE... *VICTIMS.*

"THIS ONE IS SO POWERFUL, THE WHOLE PHOTO-GRAPH SEEMS TO BE *SCREAM-ING.*

"WHY WOULD ANYONE TAKE A PHOTO OF A *BOMBED-OUT CITY* IN WORLD WAR II?"

MANY NATIVE AMERICAN CULTURES ARE UNEASY ABOUT CAMERAS, CLAIM-ING PHOTOGRAPHS CAN STEAL A PERSON'S *SOUL*...

I WONDER WHERE *FRANKLIN* FOUND HIS *SPECIAL CAMERA*...

THE CAMERA...

I HAVE BEEN *ROTTING AWAY* MINUTE BY MINUTE, YEAR BY YEAR, EVER SINCE I *LOST* THE CAMERA.

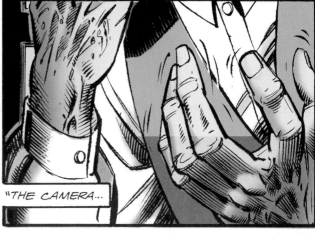

"THE CAMERA...

SOMEONE'S COMING, MULDER.

COULD BE THAT PIZZA I ORDERED.

MISTER DUBAY!

JUST CAME TO SEE WHAT YOU'VE *FOUND* AND TO OFFER ANY *HELP...*

GOT ANY *COFFEE?*

BLACK HILLS, SOUTH DAKOTA
HENRY FRANKLIN'S CABIN
5:13 P.M.

HENRY WAS ALWAYS AN *ODD DUCK...* DRIVING IN A DIFFERENT GEAR FROM THE REST OF US.

I GUESS I WAS ABOUT THE CLOSEST THING TO A *FRIEND* HE HAD...

"HE WAS A TERRIFIC PHOTOGRAPHER WITH A *BOOMING* BUSINESS...

SARSAPARILLA

CLOSED

"BUT ONE DAY, HE JUST SHUT IT ALL DOWN AND WALLED HIMSELF OFF FROM THE WORLD."

"MY HOUSE RATTLED AND SHOOK WITH THEIR CONVULSIONS...

"I COULD NOT FIGHT BACK BECAUSE I HAD NO HOPE.

"I DID NOT HAVE THE CAMERA...

"NOW, AT LAST, THE ONLY SURVIVING INCUBUS NEEDS ME...

"...CALLS TO ME.

"I MUST FIND IT."

DENY EVERYTHING™

FRANKLIN WAS A RECLUSE. AFTER ABRUPTLY CLOSING HIS SUCCESSFUL STUDIO, HE SEVERED ALL TIES TO HIS FRIENDS. THROUGHOUT THIS TIME, THE RECORDS SHOW AN UNUSUAL NUMBER OF DISAPPEARANCES IN THE AREA...

HE DIDN'T EVEN REMOVE THE IDENTIFYING PAPERS, SCULLY.

TYPICAL SERIAL KILLER. ARROGANT, OVERCONFIDENT. HE BELIEVED HE WOULD NEVER BE FOUND OUT.

MISTER DUBAY, A LOCAL, OFFERED HIS ASSISTANCE. HE ASKED MULDER TO TAKE HIS PHOTO USING FRANKLIN'S OLD EQUIPMENT. MULDER SEEMED FASCINATED WITH THE ANTIQUE CAMERA.

I SEE NO SIGNS OF TRAUMA, NO CLEAR CAUSE OF DEATH...SHE'S JUST DESSICATED, LIKE A DRIED OLD SPONGE.

AFTER THE PHOTO, DUBAY FELL STRANGELY ILL AND WENT HOME, LEAVING US TO CONTINUE OUR INVESTIGATION. FINALLY SEARCHING THE FOREST AROUND FRANKLIN'S HOUSE, WE DISCOVERED A HIDDEN ROOT CELLAR...AND TWO MUMMIFIED BODIES.

I SUSPECT WE MAY YET FIND MORE.

HEADQUARTERS CAN RUN A CHECK ON THESE TWO. MAYBE WE'LL FIND THEM ON OUR MISSING PERSONS LIST.

IN THE MEANTIME, WE NEED TO UNDERSTAND WHAT FRANKLIN WAS THINKING...

WANT YOUR PICTURE TAKEN, SCULLY?

FAMILY
PORTRAIT, part 2
The Camera Eye

THOSE ONE-STEP INSTANT CAMERAS TAKE ALL THE FUN OUT OF IT. I CAN SEE WHY FRANKLIN LOVED THIS CAMERA.

I'LL SHOW YOU MY MASTERPIECE WHEN IT'S DEVELOPED, SCULLY.

I WISH I HAD SOME OF YOUR ENERGY, MULDER. I'M GOING... TO LIE DOWN...

LET'S SEE...DO THIS STEP-BY-STEP. MAKE SURE I GET IT RIGHT THIS TIME.

WHY AM I SO TIRED...?

MAYBE COFFEE...

NEVER NOTICED BEFORE...

"...ALL THE NEARBY TREES OUTSIDE ARE DEAD OR DYING..."

MULDER...

HMMM, THE TESTAMENT OF HENRY FRANKLIN...

"After I had shot Wolff Gunthers, I took the camera and its case to a place of safety away from the bombs and away from the bullets.

"It was like no camera I had ever seen before...compelling, intriguing. I didn't know then how dangerous the camera could be... but I knew I MUST have it.

"Inside the case, I found all the supplies I needed. I didn't know what each item was, but I knew one held the greatest importance... the greatest power.

"The Jar!

"I could feel its energy, its heat --somehow alive, somehow AWARE. In a moment of foolishness, I tried to open the jar.

"But I grew suddenly frightened, not knowing my peril. I packed everything away...

"Then I planned how I would get the camera back to the U.S. after the war.

"Later, after I had learned how to use the camera, how to tap into its POWER, I opened my own studio in the Black Hills, a popular place where many strangers passed through...

SARSAPARILLA STUDIO
OLDE-TYME PHOTOGRAPHS
OPEN
WELCOME

"People were thrilled to have a unique souvenir, a photo in old-fashioned outfits...

"But the Black Hills Sioux regarded me with suspicion...

"...claiming that photographs could steal souls..."

They didn't know how close they were to the TRUTH!

"The thing in the jar grew stronger as the years went by, rewarding me with youth and energy. It seemed to be a symbiotic relationship...

"A stream of people came and went, each sacrificing a piece of their soul to feed a demonic creature a little bit at a time.

"Myself, I was just as much a parasite as it.

"For twenty years, I hadn't aged a day... but it rapidly began to catch up with me.

"It had begun to starve...and despite my own inner agony, I hardened my resolve.

"I vowed never to sacrifice another soul to it...

"But it had other plans, other puppets ...it drew them to me."

NO! GO AWAY!

"She had seen my work, and it had drawn her."

I AM NOT ACCUSTOMED TO HAVING MY WISHES DECLINED, MISTER FRANKLIN. I MUST HAVE AN ORIGINAL SARSAPARILLA STUDIOS PORTRAIT FOR MY HUSBAND. HE DOESN'T KNOW I'VE COME HERE, SO IT WILL BE QUITE A SURPRISE.

I MUST INSIST!

"I tried to fight it. I swear on my own soul... BUT I COULD NOT,

I'D BETTER WAKE UP SCULLY.

STRANGE ...SHE HASN'T MOVED AT ALL...

...NOT AT ALL!

HER SKIN...

...JUST LIKE IN FRANKLIN'S DIARY... JUST LIKE THE OLD WOMAN...

SCULLY! SCULLY, WAKE UP! SCULLY!

I HOPE THERE'S ENOUGH OF THE DARK ROOM LEFT.

I WOULDN'T WANT TO TAKE THIS DOWN TO THE FOTOMAT.

AH, SUITABLE FOR FRAMING.

APOLOGY IS POLICY ™

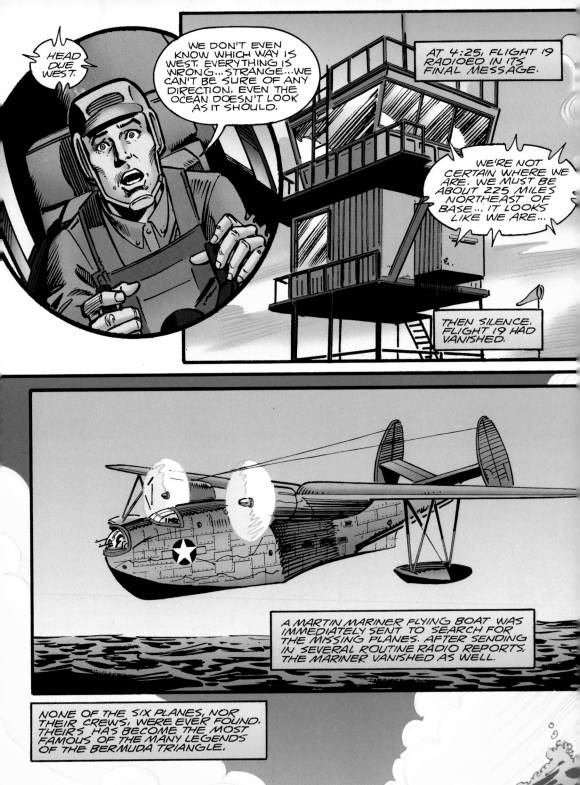

ECE,
30 PM.
CH 11, 1996.

FOR SEVEN MINUTES, THE RESIDENTS OF THIS SMALL COASTAL TOWN WATCHED WITH AWE AS THE STRANGE LIGHTS DANCED THROUGH THE SKY ABOVE THEM.

THEN WITH A BLINDING FLASH, IT WAS OVER. THE LIGHTS WERE GONE. NO ONE KNEW WHAT TO MAKE OF THEM.

IN TRUTH, ALL BUT ONE OF THE PILOTS WERE *INEXPERIENCED.*

THEIR *FLIGHT LEADER*-- UNFAMILIAR WITH THE AREA --MISTOOK THE BAHAMAS FOR THE FLORIDA KEYS AND, WITHOUT FUNCTION-ING COMPASSES AND PLAGUED BY *POOR RADIO CONTACT* WITH THE GROUND, KEPT CHANGING FLIGHT DIRECTION FROM EAST TO WEST, ALL THE WHILE DRIFTING FARTHER NORTH.

THE *WEATHER,* WHILE FINE AT TAKE-OFF, RAPIDLY *DETERIORATED* ...SO THAT WHEN THE PLANES RAN OUT OF FUEL, THE INEXPER-IENCED PILOTS WERE FORCED TO TRY A *WATER LANDING* IN THE DARK ON ROUGH SEAS IN TURBULENT WINDS.

RUTHLESS CONDITIONS, BUT NOT MYSTERIOUS.

IN THE *POPULAR VERSION* OF THIS STORY, RADIO MESSAGES WERE RECEIVED FROM THE FLIGHT SUGGESTING THAT THEY WERE EXPERIENC-ING SOMETHING OUT OF THE ORDINARY--

--EITHER A U.F.O. OR PARALLEL DIMENSION.

NONE OF THESE MESSAGES APPEAR IN THE *OFFICIAL TRANSCRIPT* OF THE MESSAGES RECEIVED.

IF THAT'S *TRUE,* THEN WHY ARE YOU *BOTHERING* WITH THIS?

THE MAN *CLAIMING* TO BE JOHN LAWRENCE IS STICKING TO THE *POPULAR VERSION* OF THE STORY, CLAIMING THAT HE AND THE OTHER PILOTS WERE, IN FACT, *ABDUCTED.*

I NEED TO BE *SURE.*

THE NIGHT BEFORE THE MAN CLAIMING TO BE LAWRENCE WASHED UP ON THE BEACH, A NUMBER OF *U.F.O.*s WERE WITNESSED BY THE RESIDENTS OF THE TOWN THAT FOUND HIM.

I'M *SKEPTICAL,* BUT THE AIR FORCE CLAIMS THAT THE OBJECT FOUND AT ROSWELL WAS A WEATHER BALLOON, NOT AN ALIEN SPACECRAFT. IF I DON'T TRUST THAT, WHY SHOULD I TRUST THIS *NAVY REPORT?*

LAWRENCE, JOHN

LAWRENCE, JOHN C.
MEDICAL REPORT
03-17-96

THE *REDSKINS* WON.

IT'S A GOOD THING THE REST OF MY SQUADRON IS STILL *MISSING*. I BET ON THE RAMS.

DO YOU REMEMBER WHO WAS PLAYING FOR THE RAMS?

AS IF IT WERE LAST WEEK, BOB WATERFIELD WAS THE QB. HE WAS *AMAZING*. HE WAS THE STAR OF THE ROSE BOWL WHEN HE PLAYED FOR UCLA.

DID YOU KNOW HE WAS MARRIED TO *JANE RUSSELL*?

THEN THERE WAS ALBIE REISZ, JACK JACOBS, STEVE NEMETH, FRED GEHRKE, JIM GILLETTE...

YOU DON'T *BELIEVE* I'M WHO I SAY I AM.

WOULD *YOU*?

PROBABLY NOT, BUT AFTER WHAT I'VE BEEN THROUGH...

WHAT EXACTLY HAVE YOU BEEN THROUGH...

I'M *STILL* NOT EXACTLY SURE.

WHERE'S THE *REST* OF FLIGHT 19?

I DON'T KNOW.

FIRST LANCE, THE SIGNATURE'S OOK AS IF EY COULD E WRITTEN THE *SAME* HAND.

THE ONE IN THE PHOTOGRAPH IS MORE *CONTROLLED*, AS IF THE WRITER WERE PURPOSE-FULLY TRYING TO KEEP IT *LEGIBLE*.

THE MORE *RECENT SIGNATURE* LOOKS LIKE IT WAS WRITTEN IN A *HURRY*, BUT THERE ARE DEFINITE PLACES WHERE THE WRITER HESITATED AND WAS UNSURE OF HIMSELF.

THIS WOULD INDICATE THAT THE PERSON HAD BEEN PRACTICING TRY-ING TO *REPLICATE* THE ORIGINAL SIGNATURE AND WAS ABLE TO APPROXIMATE IT WELL ENOUGH TO FOOL THE *CASUAL OBSERVER*, BUT WAS NOT COM-FORTABLE ENOUGH TO DO IT WITHOUT THINKING ABOUT IT.

IF THIS GUY *REALLY* SPENT THE LAST FIFTY YEARS IN A UFO LIKE HE CLAIMS, THEN THERE MIGHT NOT HAVE BEEN...

...MUCH NEED FOR HIM TO SIGN HIS NAME. HE MAY HAVE JUST *FORGOTTEN.*

THE *ORIGINALS* ARE IN THIS ENVELOPE.

THANKS, MARTHA.

'M AFRAID THAT I CAN'T ELL YOU WHO THIS FINGER-RINT BELONGS TO. WHAT I AN TELL YOU IS WHO IT *DOESN'T* BELONG TO.

DOESN'T BELONG TO ANY NOWN CRIMINAL OR FEDERAL MPLOYEE—INCLUDING MILITARY ERSONNEL—WHICH ALSO EANS THAT THIS PRINT *IDN'T* COME FROM THE MAN WHO LENT IT TO YOU, SINCE HIS RECORD'S IN *HERE.*

THE PHOTO WAS MOST LIKELY PRO-CESSED IN A HOME DARKROOM, SO IF THE PERSON WHO DEVELOPED THE PICTURE ALSO FRAMED IT, THEN IT'S PROBABLY *THEIR* PRINT.

IF THIS ERNEST CHAPMAN CLAIMS THAT PERSON WAS JOHN LAWRENCE, THEN WE HAVE A *PROBLEM* BECAUSE THIS PRINT DOESN'T MATCH THOSE WE HAVE FOR JOHN LAWRENCE IN OUR FILES.

I'M SORRY I COULDN'T BE MORE HELPFUL.

NO. ACTUALLY, YOU'VE BEEN *VERY CAREFUL.*

I'M IN TEMPLE, NEW HAMPSHIRE. THIS IS WHERE THE *CALLER* WAS FROM.

I'VE BEEN ASKING AROUND TOWN ABOUT CARL BEVERLY.

THE PEOPLE HERE AREN'T EXACTLY WARM AND OUTGOING TO START WITH, BUT AS SOON AS I MENTION HIS NAME, IT'S LIKE I BECOME *INVISIBLE*.

WHEN I STOPPED BY HIS HOUSE, I WAS TOLD BY A *NEIGHBOR* THAT THREE MEN IN BLACK PAID HIM A VISIT, AND THAT HE GOT INTO A CAR WITH THEM, AND DROVE OFF.

MAYBE YOU'VE FOUND THE *SECRET* TO BECOMING ONE OF YOUR X-FILES.

LISTEN. I HAD THE FINGERPRINTS AND THE HANDWRITING ON THAT PHOTOGRAPH *CHECKED.* THEY DON'T MATCH THOSE BELONGINGS TO THE PERSON CLAIMING TO BE JOHN LAWRENCE.

UNFORTUNATELY, I CAN'T TELL YOU *WHO* THE PRINTS ON THE PHOTO ACTUALLY BELONG TO, SO THEY MIGHT MEAN *NOTHING.* I HAVE ANOTHER IDEA I WANT TO FOLLOW UP ON...

DON'T WORRY ABOUT IT, SCULLY. I'M HOLDING A HIGH SCHOOL YEARBOOK FROM 1988. LAWRENCE'S PICTURE IS IN IT, ABOVE HIS *REAL NAME*...

...CARL BEVERLY.

GET *THIS.* IN THE SUPER-LATIVES SECTION, CARL BEVERLY WAS CHOSEN AS *BEST ACTOR.* HE HAD A LEAD ROLE IN EVERY SCHOOL PLAY.

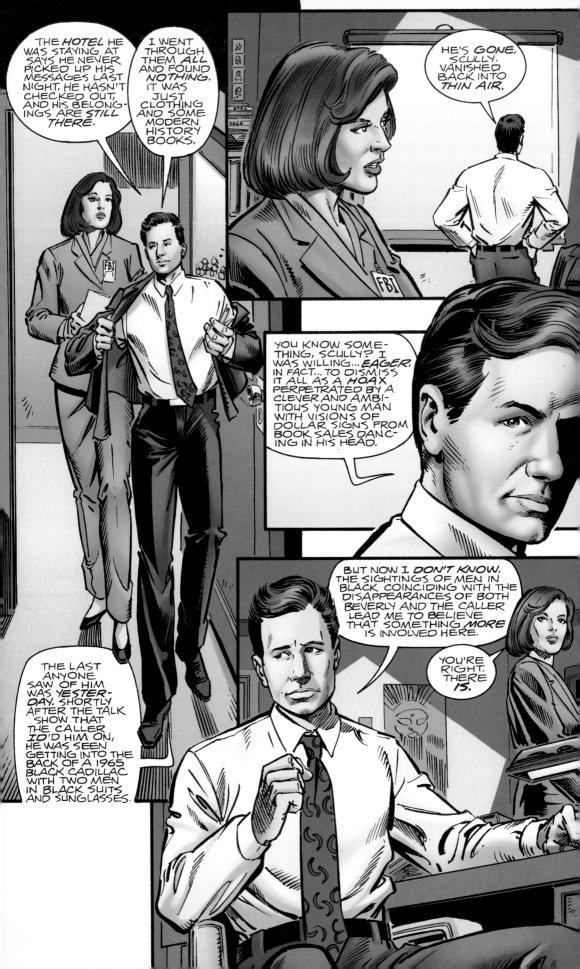

THE *HOTEL* HE WAS STAYING AT SAYS HE NEVER PICKED UP HIS MESSAGES LAST NIGHT. HE HASN'T CHECKED OUT, AND HIS BELONGINGS ARE *STILL* THERE.

I WENT THROUGH THEM *ALL* AND FOUND *NOTHING.* IT WAS JUST CLOTHING AND SOME MODERN HISTORY BOOKS.

HE'S *GONE,* SCULLY. VANISHED BACK INTO *THIN AIR.*

YOU KNOW SOMETHING, SCULLY? I WAS WILLING... *EAGER,* IN FACT... TO DISMISS IT ALL AS A *HOAX* PERPETRATED BY A CLEVER AND AMBITIOUS YOUNG MAN WITH VISIONS OF DOLLAR SIGNS FROM BOOK SALES DANCING IN HIS HEAD.

THE LAST ANYONE SAW OF HIM WAS *YESTERDAY.* SHORTLY AFTER THE TALK SHOW THAT THE CALLER *IO'D* HIM ON, HE WAS SEEN GETTING INTO THE BACK OF A 1965 BLACK CADILLAC WITH TWO MEN IN BLACK SUITS AND SUNGLASSES.

BUT NOW I *DON'T KNOW.* THE SIGHTINGS OF MEN IN BLACK COINCIDING WITH THE DISAPPEARANCES OF BOTH BEVERLY AND THE CALLER LEAD ME TO BELIEVE THAT SOMETHING *MORE* IS INVOLVED HERE.

YOU'RE RIGHT. THERE *IS.*

THE FINGERPRINT LIFTED FROM CHAPMAN'S PHOTOGRAPH *MATCHES* THOSE BELONGING TO JOHN LAWRENCE--THE *REAL* JOHN LAWRENCE. SO DOES THE *HAND*-WRITING.

HOW...?

AFTER I GOT OFF THE PHONE WITH YOU, I WENT TO VISIT A FRIEND OF MY FATHER'S.

REMEMBER WHEN I SAID THAT FLIGHT 19 RANG A BELL? WELL, I REMEMBERED *WHY.*

THESE ARE JOHN LAWRENCE'S FILES.

THE AUTHENTIC ONES.

WHERE DID YOU...?

MY FATHER HAD THIS *FRIEND*... A RETIRED NAVY CAPTAIN WHOSE POST-RETIREMENT HOBBY WAS SEARCHING FOR THE WRECKAGE OF FLIGHT 19.

SIX YEARS AGO, HE *GAVE UP;* HE DECIDED HE WAS GETTING TOO OLD TO GO CHASING AFTER *GHOSTS.*

HE HAD *COPIES* OF ALL OF THE *PERTINENT RECORDS,* WHICH HE HELD ON TO IN CASE ANYONE EVER WANTED TO PICK UP WHERE HE LEFT OFF.

HE WAS SO *ANGRY* ABOUT THE JOHN LAWRENCE IMPOSTER THAT HE WAS EAGER TO HAND THESE OVER SO THAT WE COULD *EXPOSE* HIM.

THIS GOES WAY BE-YOND TRYING TO PERPETUATE A *HOAX* AGAINST THE *PUBLIC.* SOMEONE SENT US ON A WILD GOOSE CHASE ON *PURPOSE.*

THEY HAD TO KNOW THAT SOONER OR LATER, SOMEONE WHO KNEW CARL BEVERLY WOULD RECOGNIZE HIM.

WELL...POSSIBLY THEY WERE HOPING THAT ONCE YOU DIS-COVERED THAT LAWRENCE WAS A *FRAUD,* YOU'D BE DISCOURAGED FROM CONTINUING YOUR WORK WITH SUCH *DEDICA-TION.*

THEN WHY HAVE BEVERLY-- AND THE ONLY WITNESS TO POSITIVELY IDENTIFY HIM-- *DISAPPEAR* UNDER MYSTERIOUS CIRCUM-STANCES.

WHY *BOTHER* WITH THE RETURN OF JOHN LAWRENCE IN THE FIRST PLACE?

SCULLY, WHERE'S THE *BEST* PLACE TO HIDE A BOOK?

IN A *LIBRARY.*

EXACTLY.

WHEN ONE PERSON CLAIMS TO BE THE LOVE CHILD OF ELVIS PRESLEY IT'S A POSSIBILITY. WHEN A BUNCH OF PEOPLE CLAIM THE SAME THING IT BECOMES AN *UNFUNNY JOKE.*

SO WHAT YOU'RE SAYING IS THAT SOMEONE *DELIBERATELY* SENT OUT A FAKE JOHN LAWRENCE, SO THAT ANYONE ELSE CLAIMING TO BE JOHN LAWRENCE WOULD BE *SCOFFED* AT?

WHY GO THROUGH THE TROUBLE *REPLACING* ALL OF LAWRENCE'S RECORDS IF THEY KNEW THAT BEVERLY WOULD BE EXPOSED AS AN *IMPOSTER,* ANYWAY?

DOING SO CLEARLY SUGGESTS THAT THERE'S SOME-THING *DEEPER* GOING ON.

AND BY HAVING HIS IMPOSTER *VANISH MYSTERIOUSLY,* YOU MAKE HIS CLAIMS ALL THE MORE POSSIBLE. A NEW JOHN LAWRENCE'S CREDIBILITY WOULD BE *LAUGHABLE.*

WHAT MAKES YOU THINK A *SECOND PERSON* MIGHT COME ALONG, CLAIMING TO BE JOHN LAWRENCE?

BECAUSE I THINK MAYBE THE REAL JOHN LAWRENCE *HAS* RETURNED AND WHOEVER SET THIS HOAX UP KNOWS IT.

IF HE *IS* BACK AND HE'S AS YOUNG AS WHEN HE DISAP-PEARED, I'D LIKE TO KNOW HOW HE *STAYED* THAT WAY.

IT WASN'T UNTIL <u>THAT POINT</u> THAT I TRULY UNDERSTOOD MULDER'S UNFLAGGING INTEREST IN THE JOHN LAWRENCE MYSTERY. IT GAVE HIM <u>HOPE</u>. DURING HIS SEARCH FOR HIS MISSING SISTER, MULDER HAD BEEN FEELING THE CONSTANT PRESSURE OF A TICKING CLOCK. HE WAS RACING AGAINST <u>TIME</u>.

IF LAWRENCE HAD REALLY BEEN ABDUCTED AND RE-TURNED UNAGED AFTER HAVING BEEN MISSING FOR 51 YEARS, THEN WHY WOULDN'T THE <u>SAME</u> HOLD FOR SAMANTHA WHO'S ONLY BEEN MISSING FOR THIRTEEN?

IF SHE RETURNED AS A NINE-YEAR-OLD GIRL, SHE'D FINALLY GET TO EXPERIENCE THE CHILDHOOD OF WHICH SHE WAS ROBBED. SHE'D RETURN AS THE <u>SISTER</u> MULDER REMEMBERED LOSING.

I LEAVE MY SKEPTICISM <u>UNSPOKEN</u>. MULDER NEEDS HIS FAITH.

BUT IF LAWRENCE HAS <u>TRULY RETURNED</u>, THERE'S BEEN NO SIGN, AND NEITHER OF US HAS ANY IDEA WHERE TO LOOK.

...UNDERSTAND YOUR DESIRES TO RETURN <i>HOME</i> AND TO SEE YOUR FAMILIES. I MUST ASK YOU TO CONTINUE YOUR <i>PATIENCE</i>. THERE IS STILL MUCH YOU MUST LEARN AND PREPARE FOR BEFORE YOU ARE RETURNED TO THE WORLD. <i>DISMISSED</i>.

EVERY ONE OF THEM IS ACCOUNTED FOR. THE <i>ENTIRE FLIGHT</i>.

SO HOW LONG DO YOU THINK BEFORE THEY CAN GO <i>HOME</i>?

HOME?

THEY CAN <i>NEVER</i> BE ALLOWED TO LEAVE.

FROM NOW ON, <i>THIS</i> IS THEIR HOME.

Taylor,
Powers, Edward J.
Gerber, For__ J.
Stivers
Lawrenc__
Bossi, J__
Swan

THE END